Disney

Winnie the Pooh

Fun-filled Activities

Complete the activities, then flip the book
over to read a wonderful story!

PaRragon

Bath · New York · Singapore · Hong Kong · Cologne · Delhi
Melbourne · Amsterdam · Johannesburg · Auckland · Shenzhen

Copy colour

Winnie the Pooh loves honey more than anything. Use this picture as a guide, then colour Pooh on the opposite page.

Perfect match

It's sunny in the Hundred-Acre Wood. Can you match each friend to his shadow?

1

2

3

4

A

B

C

D

Answers on page 31

4

Spot the difference

Pooh and his pals are having fun with their balloons. Can you spot three differences between the pictures?

Answers on page 31

Playtime!

Pooh and Piglet are playing a game of Pooh Sticks. Join in the game by colouring them in.

Bouncy fun!

Tigger and Roo love to bounce! Colour in this lovely picture.

Look closely!

Can you match each close-up to its owner?

1

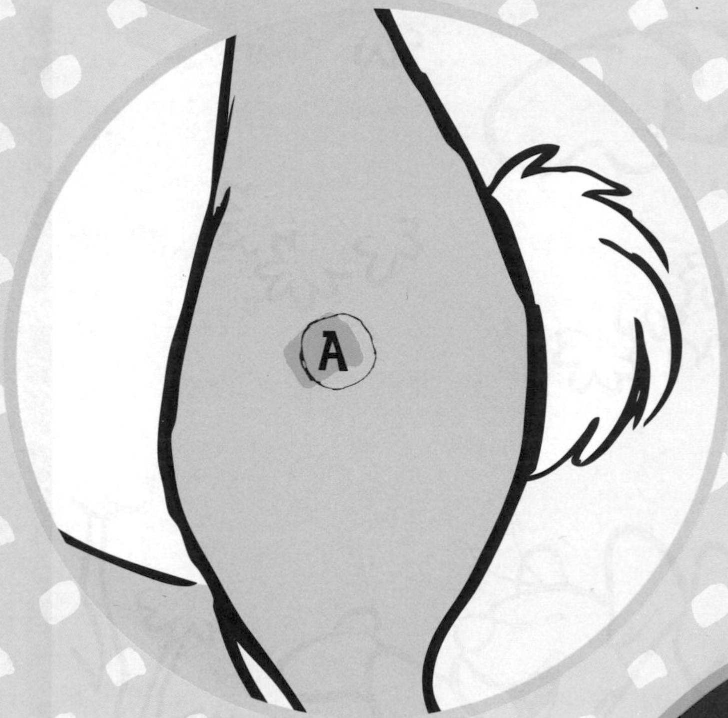

A

B

2

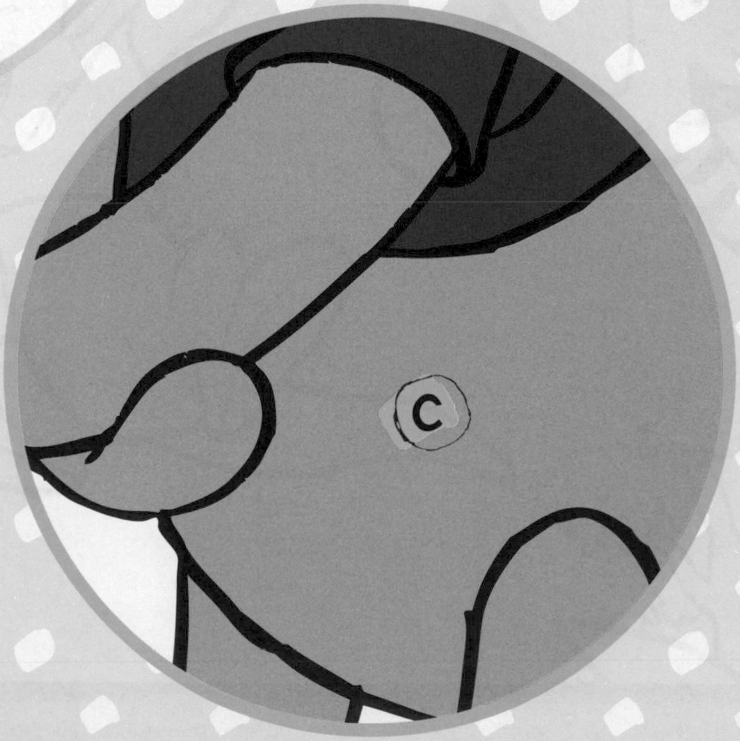

C

3

Answers on page 31

8

Woodland maze

Pooh is looking for Kanga and Roo, but they are playing deep in the Hundred-Acre Wood. Can you help Pooh find his friends?

Answer on page 31

9

Cheer up Eeyore!

"Thanks for noticin' me".
Brighten up Eeyore's
day by colouring him
in on the opposite
page. Use the picture
below as a guide.

10

Memory test

Have a close look at this picture. Count to ten, then turn over the page and see if you can remember what the missing items are.

POOH'S THOTFUL SPOT

Memory test

Did you look closely at the picture on the previous page? There are three things missing from this picture. Can you tell what they are?

SANDERS

RNIG ALSO

POOH'S THOTFUL SPOT

Answers on page 31

Puddle fun!

Tigger and Roo love splashing in puddles. Colour in this fun-filled picture.

Cooking time

Pooh, Piglet and Tigger are baking a cake for Eeyore. Can you name the objects that are circled in the picture? Now fill in the missing letters.

1 _ _ at

2 E _ _ _

3 H _ n _ y

4 _ _ traw _ erry

Answers on page 31

Thinking spot

Pooh is thinking very hard. Help him think by colouring this picture.

17

Tigger-ific!

Tiggers are always bouncing everywhere! Use this picture as a guide, then copy it by colouring in Tigger on the opposite page.

Spot the difference

Tigger, Pooh and Piglet are having a snack. Can you circle three differences in the bottom picture?

20

Answers on page 31

Hunny hunt

Pooh would like some honey. Perhaps Owl can help? Guide Pooh through the maze to Owl.

Answer on page 31

Memory test

Look closely at this picture. Now count to ten and cover it up. How many objects can you remember?

Honey Pots

Can you find these objects on the previous page? Circle the things in the picture when you find them.

Mushrooms

Rainbow

Butterfly

Answers on page 31

Match the tiggers

Look closely at these pictures of Tigger. Can you tell which two are the same? Put a tick next to your two answers.

A

B

C

D

E

Answers on page 31

Close-up match

Can you match each close–up to its owner?

Answer on page 31

25

Draw Piglet

Use the grid to help you draw Piglet on the opposite page. Then colour him in!

Count on me!

See how many pictures of Eeyore you can count. Write your answer in the box below.

My answer:

Answers on page 31

28

Tigger Tigger

How many times can you find 'Tigger' in the word grid? Look up, down, backwards and forwards.

P	I	T	I	G	G	E	R
L	G	I	G	L	A	I	Y
T	I	G	G	E	R	A	T
I	G	G	C	Z	C	R	I
G	S	E	R	A	B	S	G
G	A	R	U	O	I	A	G
E	L	D	L	Z	R	B	E
R	G	T	I	G	G	E	R

Number of tiggers:

Answers on page 31

29

Picture perfect

Draw a picture of your favourite Hundred-Acre Wood friend in the frame below. Then colour it in!

Answers

Page 4
1-C
2-B
3-A
4-D

Page 5

Page 8
1-C
2-B
3-A

Page 9

Page 12
A-1
B-2
C-4
D-3

Page 14

Page 16
1. hat
2. ear
3. honey
4. strawberry

Page 20

Page 21

Page 23

Page 24
C and D

Page 25
1-B
2-C
3-A

Page 28
5

Page 29

P	I	T	I	G	G	E	R
L	G	I	G	L	A	I	Y
T	I	G	G	E	R	A	T
I	G	G	C	Z	C	R	I
G	S	E	R	A	B	S	G
G	A	R	U	O	I	A	G
E	L	D	L	Z	R	B	E
R	G	T	I	G	G	E	R

6

31

Now **close** the book and **flip it over** to **read** a **wonderful story** – *Somebody's Treasure.*

Wonderful Story

Read the story, then flip the book over
to complete some fun-filled activities!

First published by Parragon in 2012
Parragon
Queen Street House
4 Queen Street
Bath BA1 1HE, UK
www.parragon.com

Written by K. Emily Hutta
Illustrated by Carson Van Osten, John Kurtz & the Disney Storybook Artists
Edited by Samantha Crockford
Designed by Karl Tall
Production by Sarah Brown

ISBN 978-1-4454-4805-3

Printed in China

Disney
Winnie the Pooh

Somebody's Treasure

Bath • New York • Singapore • Hong Kong • Cologne • Delhi
Melbourne • Amsterdam • Johannesburg • Auckland • Shenzhen

It was springtime in the Hundred-Acre Wood. The flowers were budding, the birds were chirping and Winnie the Pooh was doing a bit – really just a very little bit – of spring-cleaning.

"One ... thing ... at a time," Pooh said to himself, puffing as he bent over his somewhat-rounder-than-average tummy to pick up a cracked honeypot.

"I'll just put this pot outside for now. That will be quite enough spring-cleaning for one day."

As Pooh stepped out of his front door, balancing the pot and trying very hard not to tip over, a cheery voice called out to him.

"Hello, Pooh," Kanga said, waving.

"Halloooo," Pooh said. He tried to wave back, but the pot teetered wildly and he had to use both hands to keep it from falling.

"I'm getting rid of this useless old thing," Pooh explained. "A honeypot that won't hold honey is no good to me."

"Oh, may I have it?" Kanga asked. "I can use it as a planter for my spring flowers!"

"Yes!" Pooh said eagerly. "But it's cracked, you know." Pooh believed that a bear should always be honest about such things.

"Oh, that's good," Kanga said.

"It is?" Pooh asked, quite surprised.

"The cracks will let the extra water run out," Kanga said. "That's just what a planter should do."

Pooh waved until Kanga was out of sight. "Who could have guessed that my useless old pot would turn out to be Kanga's perfect new planter?" Pooh asked himself. When no one answered, he shrugged. Some things were just meant to remain mysteries.

Suddenly, a loud grumble sounded from somewhere close by. Pooh nodded.

"I see what you mean," he said to his tummy. "Spring-cleaning does make a bear awfully hungry. I think it may be – in fact I'm quite certain it is – time for a little smackerel."

While Pooh was busy licking honey from his paws, Kanga was walking past Rabbit's house. Rabbit was sitting in the sun, brushing his tail and muttering.

"Did you say something, Rabbit?" Kanga asked.

"I said that this happens every spring," Rabbit complained. "When I clear the weeds from my garden patch, I get thistles in my tail and holes in my coveralls."

"Well, when you're finished brushing your tail, why don't you come to my house?" Kanga said kindly. "I can sew patches on those coveralls for you."

Rabbit brushed and brushed until every thistle was pulled out, along with quite a bit of soft, puffy fur from his tail.

"Rather nice, if I do say so myself," Rabbit said, admiring his reflection in the window. "Now if Kanga can help me patch my coveralls, I'll be as good as new."

As soon as Rabbit left, a shy little bird swooped down and gathered some of the soft fluff from Rabbit's brush. She flew with it to a nearby tree where she was building a nest.

Back and forth she went until she had the cosiest nest in the Hundred-Acre Wood. Her chicks would be so snug and warm – and all because Rabbit had got thistles in his tail!

Kanga was busy sorting through her sewing basket when Rabbit arrived at her house. She pointed to a small pile of brightly coloured fabric scraps.

"These bits and pieces are left over from some of the sewing projects I did over the winter," Kanga said. "Don't you think they'll be just right for your patches?"

"Oh, yes!" Rabbit cried. "And these would make great pockets for my apron!" he said, sorting through the bright squares of fabric. "And this one would be perfect for a new handkerchief! Oh, how am I going to decide?"

"Take them all," Kanga said, laughing. "I don't need them. I'm happy to find someone who can use them."

With fresh patches sewn onto his coveralls and his pockets stuffed with, well, with more patches, Rabbit was heading towards home when he bumped into Eeyore.

"I'm terribly sorry," Eeyore said. "I don't know how I overlooked you with all of those, those, ummmm...."

"They're patches. And pockets. And this one is a kerchief," Rabbit said proudly. "Kanga gave them to me."

Eeyore studied his friend for a long moment. "They're surprisingly cheerful," Eeyore said. "I don't suppose Kanga has anything I could use to brighten things up for spring."

"Brighten things up? You?" Rabbit said doubtfully. "Well, I guess it can't hurt to try."

And so it was that Eeyore visited Kanga that morning, too. And if it took him a rather longish time to choose from among Kanga's leftover ribbons – even with all the helpful advice he got from Roo – well, no one was in any sort of hurry anyway.

It was early afternoon in the Hundred-Acre Wood by the time Eeyore walked by Piglet's house. Piglet was sweeping a pile of haycorn caps out of the door.

"Something's different about you, Eeyore," said Piglet.

"I've got a little spruced up for spring," Eeyore said.

"You look splendid!" Piglet said. "You look like you could be going to a party! In fact, a party is a very good idea. That is, I've made enough haycorn muffins for a party – if only I had a picnic table where everyone could sit. It would be a shame to sit inside on such a lovely spring day. Don't you agree, Eeyore?"

"Yes," Eeyore said, nodding slowly. "And I think maybe I can help."

A short while later, Piglet was amazed to see a large wooden crate coming down the path towards his house. The crate had an assortment of legs, one rather sproingy-looking tail and writing on the side that said "FRADGIL". Piglet ran inside and peeked through a crack in his door, just in case the crate was up to no good.

"Hoo-hoo-hoo!" the crate shouted as it got closer. "Where are you?"

Piglet was too frightened to answer.

"I just knew this would happen," the crate said in a completely different and somewhat gloomy voice. "He was here a little while ago and now he's gone."

"Yes, well, perhaps if we put this down, we'll be able to find him," the crate said, rather sensibly.

Piglet watched wide-eyed as the crate tilted to the side and out came Tigger, Eeyore and Owl!

"Oh, it's you!" Piglet cried happily, running outside to greet them.

"Well, who did you think it was?" Tigger asked.

Piglet really couldn't say.

"Owl got an enormormerous box of books the other day, and he doesn't need the crate anymore," Tigger said. "Don't you think it will make a splendiferous picnic table?"

"Oh, yes!" Piglet said. "If you would put it down right over there, I'll invite the rest of our friends for haycorn muffins and tea."

In no time at all, Piglet's friends were gathered around his splendid new picnic table enjoying a springtime, mid-afternoon tea party.

"You must have been baking all morning," Pooh said politely. But what actually came out was, "Moo muf huf bibakeen ow mowmin." Because, as everyone knows, it is difficult for a bear to pronounce his words properly with a mouth full of haycorn muffin.

Owl noticed the pile of haycorn caps outside Piglet's door. "Those would be just the thing to make new draughts for my draught set," Owl said. "Let's try them out, Roo. Most of mine rolled through the cracks and bounced out of the windows when I played draughts with Tigger over the winter."

"Well, a tigger has to bounce once in a while," Tigger said. "Even if he is playing draughts."

The friends lingered long into
the soft light of evening. It had
been such a wonderful day –
such a surprising and useful
sort of day – that no one
wanted it to end.

Piglet sighed happily, admiring the way that his friends fitted around his new table. Rabbit and Eeyore looked so festive in their new finery. Kanga was chatting about her new planter. Owl was playing draughts on the tablecloth with Roo. And absolutely everyone seemed to be enjoying Piglet's delicious haycorn muffins – especially Winnie the Pooh.

A Nature Activity

Here's a wonderful nature activity for parents and children to do together.

Somebody's Treasure tells the story of how the friends in the Hundred-Acre Wood found new uses for things that someone else didn't want or need. For example, Kanga used Pooh's broken old honeypot to plant flowers.

You can also reuse things that you find around your own house to plant flowers. Egg boxes make wonderful places to grow baby plants from seeds. Just poke some holes in the bottom of the egg box, put potting soil and a seed in each section, place the box in a sunny spot and then water regularly until the seedlings begin to grow.

When the plants get too big for their egg-box home, you can reuse old drink containers (cut them in half, put holes in the bottom and fill them with soil) as planters for your young plants. Or you can use a cracked old honeypot – it's really up to you!

The End

Now *close the book*
and *flip it over* for some
activity adventures!